This book belongs to

....

This is the story of Jack Pott.

You can read a little or read a lot!

There's something else.

Can you guess what?

Throughout this book, there's

a flowerpot to spot.

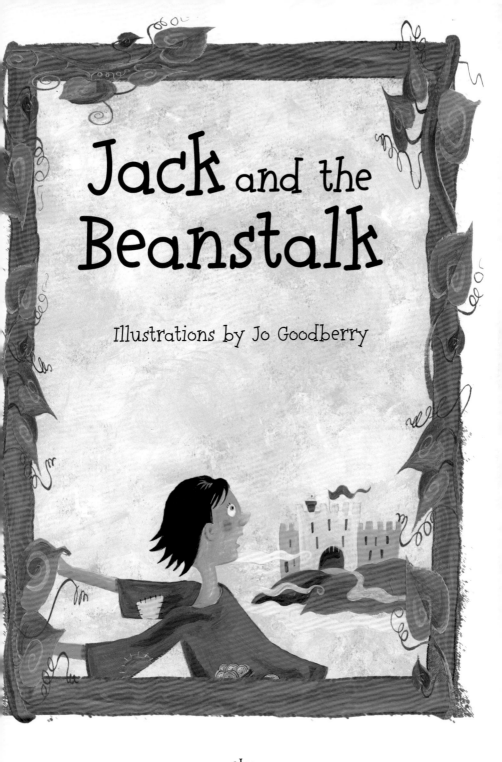

Jack and the Beanstalk

Illustrations by Jo Goodberry

make
believe
ideas

Jack Pott is poor. He lives with his mom and a cow called Moo.

Moo is not producing milk.
"Go and sell Moo at the
market," says Jack's mom.
Jack sells Moo for some
magic beans.

"Look what I got!" says
Jack. He shows his mom
the beans. She is angry
and throws the beans
out the window.

The next morning, Jack
sees a huge beanstalk
in the garden.

Jack climbs up the beanstalk. At the top, there is a castle.

"Someone BIG lives here," says Jack. He sees a chest full of gold! Jack grabs some of the gold.

A giant marches in.
He is as tall as a tree
and as big as a bus!

The giant roars:
"Fee, fi, fo, fum,
I smell the blood
of an Englishman."

The giant spots Jack.
Jack runs out of the castle.
The giant falls over.

Jack runs to the beanstalk.
He starts to climb down.

Jack hears the giant roar . . .

"Fee, fi, fo, fum,
I smell the blood
of an Englishman."

Jack reaches the bottom
of the beanstalk. He
points at the giant.
"Get an axe!" Jack
shouts to his mom.

The giant roars again:
"Fee, fi, fo, fum,
I smell the blood
of an English *mom!*"

Jack and his mom
chop down the
beanstalk.

The giant falls to the ground, dead!

Jack shows his mom the gold. "Look! We are rich!" she says.

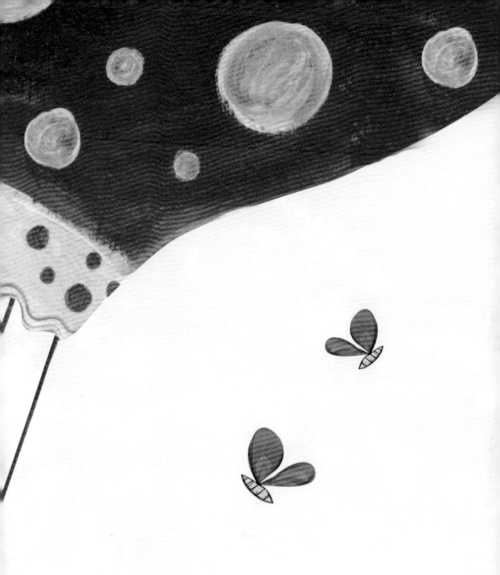

Jack buys back Moo.
His mom buys a
hot-air balloon!

Ready to tell

Oh no! Some of the pictures from this story have gotten mixed up! Can you retell the story and point to each picture in the correct order?

Picture dictionary

Encourage your child to read these words from the story and gradually develop his or her basic vocabulary.

axe

beanstalk

castle

flowerpot

giant

market

mom

points

window

Key words

Here are some key words used in context. Help your child to use other words from the border in simple sentences.

Jack lives with his **mom**.

He sells Moo **at** the market.

He climbs **up** the beanstalk.

"**Look!**" says Jack.

They have lots **of** gold.

Gold

Decorate a Dotty pot!

You may not be able to grow a giant beanstalk, but why not decorate a flowerpot and grow a plant of your own?

You will need

- a medium-sized terracotta flowerpot and pot holder
- powder or poster paints in different colors
- craft glue • plastic cups • paintbrush

What to do

1 Make sure your flowerpot is clean and dry.

2 You are going to decorate the pot with paint mixed with craft glue. For each color mix $1/3$ glue to $2/3$ paint in a plastic cup. Use this to give the pot a waterproof and shiny "varnish" effect.

3 Paint the pot and holder with a base coat of one color and leave to dry.

4 When dry, use different colors to paint patterns on top of the base coat. You might like to make it as dotty as one of Jack's mom's dresses. Or you could paint it black-and-white like Moo the cow. Leave until dry.

5 Find out at your local garden center what will grow at this time of year. (Perhaps they will say "magic beans!") Follow their advice about how to plant the bulb or seeds they suggest.

6 Water the pot regularly and wait for the plant to grow.